Supporting
Writing Skills

FOR AGES **6–7**

Andrew Brodie

Introduction

Supporting Writing Skills is aimed at all those who work with children who have been identified as needing 'additional' or 'different' literacy support. It can be used by anyone working with children who fall into this category, whether you are a teacher, classroom assistant or parent.

Typically the six to seven year-old children for whom the book is intended will be working at the levels expected of Reception or Year 1 children or may simply need extra help in tackling the level of work appropriate for Year 2. Their difficulties may be short term, and overcome with extra practice and support on a one-to-one or small group basis, or they may be long term, where such support enables them to make progress but at a level behind their peer group.

The activities in this book provide exactly what these children need – plenty of writing activities linked to the work that they will be completing in other areas of the curriculum. All the activities provide excellent opportunities for speaking and listening and most pages include reading practice in addition to the main writing task. Each activity page includes brief 'Notes for teachers' so that the pages can be picked up and used quickly and effectively.

The 2006 Framework for teaching Literacy lists twelve strands for literacy development. Strands 1 to 4 concern Speaking and Listening; Strands 5 to 12 concern Reading and Writing. The writing activities in this book have been created to match many of the key elements of the Framework's reading and writing strands for Foundation Stage, Year 1 and Year 2:

5. Apply phonic knowledge and skills as the prime approach to reading and spelling unfamiliar words that are not completely decodable; read and spell phonically decodable two-syllable and three-syllable words; spell with increasing accuracy and confidence, drawing on word recognition and knowledge of word structure, and spelling patterns
6. Spell new words using phonics as the prime approach; segment sounds into their constituent phonemes in order to spell them correctly; spell with increasing accuracy and confidence, drawing on word recognition and knowledge of word structure, and spelling patterns including common inflections and use of double letters
7. Extend their vocabulary, exploring the meanings and sounds of new words; show an understanding of the elements of stories, such as main character, sequence of events; explain organisational features of texts, including alphabetical order, layout, diagrams, captions
8. Visualise and comment on events, characters and ideas making imaginative links to their own experiences
9. Use key features of narrative in their own writing; convey information and ideas in simple non-narrative forms; find and use new and interesting words and phrases, including story language; create short simple texts on paper that combine words with images; select from different presentational features to suit particular writing purposes
10. Write chronological and non-chronological texts using simple structures; use planning to establish clear sections for writing
11. Compose and write simple sentences independently to communicate meaning; use capital letters and full stops when punctuating simple sentences
12. Write legibly, using upper and lower case letters appropriately within words, and observing correct spacing within and between words.

Children generally achieve the greatest success in an atmosphere of support and encouragement. Praise from a caring adult can be the best reward for the children's efforts. The worksheets and activities in this book will provide many opportunities for children to enjoy these successes. The development of a positive attitude and the resulting increase in self-esteem will help them with all of their schoolwork.

This book consists of three main sections:

Section 1 (pages 6–29)

Worksheets 1 to 24 contain activities to encourage the process of spelling new words, including some that will be needed for work across the curriculum, through use of phonic skills. Worksheets 6 to 24 provide many opportunities for creating simple sentences. Sentences with clear punctuation are modelled for the pupils, then the activities promote the construction of accurate sentences that start with capital letters and end with full stops. Some pages require pupils to write just one sentence, using relevant vocabulary, while others require several sentences on a particular theme.

Section 2 (pages 31–47)

With two sets of narrative sheets, pupils are encouraged to work out the correct sequence of a set of sentences and to combine these with the images provided. From this speaking, listening and reading activity the children move on to rewriting the text within a simple 'book' presentation. Further templates are provided to enable the children to create independent texts.

Section 3 (pages 51–64)

An important resource contained within this book is the dictionary that can be created from the final fourteen sheets. This contains all the high frequency words recommended for Reception, Year 1 and Year 2, together with all the additional words used in this book. We suggest that you complete Worksheets 1 to 4, which provide practice of the alphabet, before creating this resource. The dictionary can be used by the children when working on the worksheets.

Each page of the dictionary has spaces for pupils to write their own spellings – this is an excellent way of encouraging the children to use their phonic knowledge to spell new words. When a child needs a word, help her/him to find the correct page of the dictionary then ask her/him to attempt the word by segmenting it into its phonemes. Give the child lots of praise where s/he is successful even in part of a word then write the word correctly on the line next to her/his attempt, stressing the phonemes and pointing out the graphemes that represent these.

Contents

Record and Review

Name: ______________________ Date of birth: ____________

Teacher: ______________________ Class: ____________

Support assistant: ______________________

Code of Practice stage: ______________________ Date targets set: ____________

Target

1 ______________________

2 ______________________

3 ______________________

4 ______________________

Review

Target

1 ______________________

____

______________________ Target achieved? ☐ Date: ____________

2 ______________________

____

______________________ Target achieved? ☐ Date: ____________

3 ______________________

____

______________________ Target achieved? ☐ Date: ____________

4 ______________________

____

______________________ Target achieved? ☐ Date: ____________

Name: Date:

Here is the alphabet.

a b c d e f g h i j k l m n o p q r s t u v w x y z

Join the letters of the alphabet to make a picture.

z a y b x c w d v e u f t p o l q k s r n m j g i h

Notes for teachers

Children need lots of opportunities to speak and to listen before they can become effective writers. Discuss the alphabet with the child, saying the names of the letters and the sounds that they make. Help her/him to join the dots to reveal a picture of a rocket.

Name: Date:

Copy the letters of the alphabet.

a b c d e f g

h i j k l m n

o p q r s t u

v w x y z

Notes for teachers

Discuss the alphabet with the child, saying the names of the letters and the sounds that they make. Help her/him to write the letters of the alphabet. You may like to demonstrate how to form each letter using the school's handwriting style. Watch closely as the child writes each letter to ensure that s/he is forming it correctly. Encourage her/him to write the letters in the correct positions on the lines provided, with the descenders passing through the lines.

Name: **Date:**

Here is the alphabet in capital letters.

A B C D E F G H I J K L M N O P Q R S T U V W X Y Z

Join the capital letters to make a picture.

A B C D E F G H I J K L M N O P Q R S T U V W X Y Z

Notes for teachers

Discuss the alphabet with the child, saying the names of the letters and the sounds that they make. Point out that these letters are capital letters and that we always use capital letters at the start of a sentence and for special words, such as people's names. Help her/him to join the dots to reveal a picture of a space ship.

Name: Date:

Copy the capital letters of the alphabet.

A B C D E F G

H I J K L M N

O P Q R S T U

V W X Y Z

Notes for teachers

Revise the alphabet with the child, saying the names of the letters and the sounds that they make. Help her/him to write the capital letters. You may like to demonstrate how to form each letter using the school's handwriting style. Watch closely as the child writes each letter to ensure that s/he is forming it correctly. Encourage her/him to write the letters in the correct positions on the lines provided.

Name: Date:

Join the pairs of letters.

The first one has been done for you.

A e f n m

O

S C B

H I p

z

l a

r

E D G s y

o

q

b X Q

U

T c d F

W

R

i w M

J v

Y K P

j

g u

Z k

V N

L h

x t

Notes for teachers

Revise the alphabet with the child, saying the names of the letters and the sounds that they make. It is essential that s/he can recognise the capital letter equivalent of each lower case letter. Help her/him to draw lines to join the lower case letters to the matching capital letters.

Name: **Date:**

This is Zipper. He comes from space. He is an alien. He has two noses. Label the picture of Zipper using these words: *eye, ear, nose.*

Notes for teachers

Children need lots of opportunities to speak and to listen before they can become effective writers. Discuss the picture of Zipper and read the sentences together with the child. Point out the capital letters at the start of each sentence and at the start of the name Zipper, and the full stop at the end of each sentence. On this sheet, where the prime aim is to introduce the character, the writing task is quite simple.

Name: **Date:**

What could Zipper be saying to you?

Notes for teachers

Help the child to read the question sentence. Point out that it starts with a capital letter because all sentences do, that it has a capital letter for the name Zipper and that it has a question mark instead of a full stop at the end because it is a question. Discuss with the child what s/he thinks Zipper could be saying e.g. 'My name is Zipper. I come from space. I am an alien. What is your name?' The child may only be able to write one sentence or may think of several. S/he should write with legible writing in accordance with the school's handwriting policy. It might help if you write the sentence first for her/him to copy to ensure that the letters are formed correctly with clear ascenders and descenders. Encourage the child to start each sentence with a capital letter and to end it with a full stop or with a question mark if appropriate.

Name: **Date:**

What could you say to Zipper?

Notes for teachers

Help the child to read the question sentence. Point out that it starts with a capital letter because all sentences do, that it has a capital letter for the name Zipper and that it has a question mark instead of a full stop because it is a question. Ask the child to draw a picture of her/himself in the space on the right with her/his mouth next to the appropriate part of the speech bubble. Discuss with the child what s/he could be saying to Zipper e.g. 'My name is... I come from... I am a boy/girl.' The child may only be able to write one sentence or may think of several. S/he should write with legible writing in accordance with the school's handwriting policy. It might help if you write the sentence first for her/him to copy to ensure that the letters are formed correctly with clear ascenders and descenders. Encourage the child to start each sentence with a capital letter and to end it with a full stop or with a question mark if appropriate. The finished sheet can be placed beside Worksheet 7 as though Zipper and the child are having a conversation.

Name: Date:

This is Zipper's face.
He has three eyes,
two ears, two noses
and one mouth.

Draw your face.

Write about your face.

Notes for teachers

Discuss the picture of Zipper's face with the child and read the text, saying the words very clearly so that s/he can hear the phonemes within each word. Point out the capital letters at the start of each sentence and for the name Zipper, and the full stops at the end of the sentences. The second sentence also has commas because it includes a list of facial features. Read this sentence to the child using appropriate stresses and pauses to demonstrate the presence of the commas. Help the child to think about her/his own face and to create a sentence e.g. I have two eyes, two ears, one nose and one mouth.

Name: **Date:**

This is Zipper.

He has two legs and four arms.

He looks friendly.

Draw yourself.

Write about yourself.

Notes for teachers

Discuss the picture with the child and read the text, saying the words very clearly so that s/he can hear the phonemes within each word. Point out the capital letters at the start of each sentence and for the name Zipper, and the full stops at the end of each sentence. Help the child to create some sentences about herself/himself e.g. This is a picture of me. I have two legs and two arms. I look friendly.

Name: **Date:**

Zipper comes from space. He is looking at a house. He hasn't seen a house before.

Write sentences to tell Zipper about the house.

Notes for teachers

This activity provides the opportunity for the child to write information in a simple non-narrative form that could be linked with the Science topic, materials. Discuss the small picture of Zipper with the child and read the text, saying the words very clearly so that s/he can hear the phonemes within each word. When s/he is ready, discuss the house picture and what could be written on the lines. Encourage the children to compose a full sentence for each line. The words in the word bank would enable her/him to write the following sentences, though s/he may think of other sentences that are just as appropriate. 'The walls are made of bricks. The roof is made of tiles. The windows are made of glass.'

Name: Date:

Draw a house.

Write about your house picture.

Notes for teachers

This sheet provides the opportunity for the child to write information in a simple non-narrative form that could be linked with the Science topic, materials. Discuss the child's picture of a house, encouraging her/him to put in as many details as possible e.g. the front door, the letterbox, the windows, the chimney, etc. You may like to take the child outside to look at a house and to discuss some of the details. When s/he writes about the picture s/he could make use of the dictionary that has been created from the Resource sheets on pages 51–64.

Name: ______________________ Date: ______

Zipper has a spaceship.
Write the correct names
for all of these vehicles.

WORD BANK

crane
spaceship
bus
fire engine
bike
car
motorbike
lorry
van

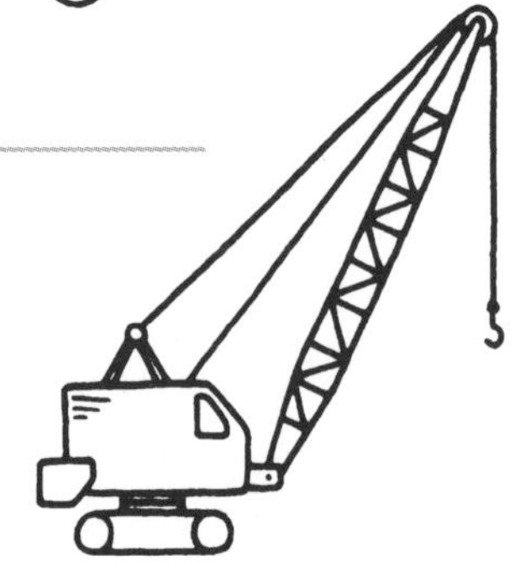

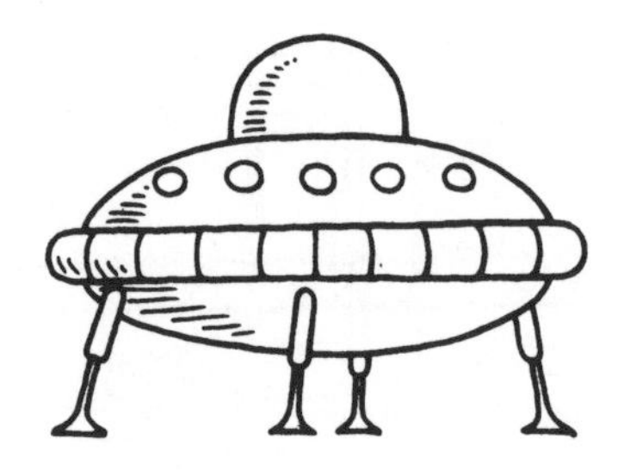

Notes for teachers

This sheet, together with Worksheet 14, provides an opportunity for the child to practise vocabulary that can be used in her/his everyday writing and that is linked with the DT topic, vehicles. After completing the worksheet, help the child to write each of the words on the appropriate page of the dictionary that has been created from the Resource sheets on pages 51–64. S/he could attempt to write the words without looking, using phonic skills of segmenting words into phonemes, and then checking by looking at this worksheet. As an extension activity the child could cut out all of the pictures from this sheet and from Worksheet 14 then sort them into groups, such as: emergency vehicles, vehicles used for building, passenger vehicles, etc. Again, this provides an excellent opportunity for speaking and listening.

Name: **Date:**

Write the correct names for all these vehicles.

WORD BANK

police car
ambulance
tractor
taxi
dumper truck
caravan
trailer
digger
minibus

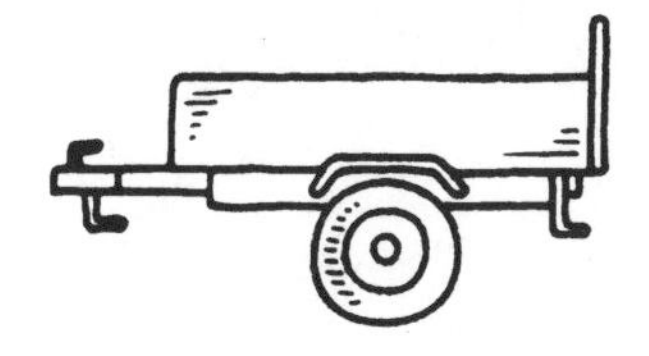

Notes for teachers

This activity sheet, together with Worksheet 13, provides the opportunity for the child to practise vocabulary that can be used in her/his everyday writing and that is linked with the DT topic, vehicles. After completing the worksheet, support the child in writing each of the words on the appropriate page of the dictionary that has been created from the Resource sheets on pages 51–64. The child could attempt to write the words without looking, using phonic skills of segmenting words into phonemes, and then checking by looking at this worksheet. As an extension activity the child could cut out all of the pictures from this sheet and from Worksheet 13 then sort them into groups, such as: emergency vehicles, vehicles used for building, passenger vehicles etc. Again, this provides an excellent opportunity for speaking and listening.

Name: Date:

Zipper is looking at three cars.

Listen to your teacher. Write the sentences.

Notes for teachers

Encourage the child to spell words by segmenting them into their phonemes by dictating two sentences to her/him: *There are three cars. The big car is next to the little car*. The child is likely to need help with segmenting the words into their phonemes and you can provide further support by helping her/him to look up the words in the dictionary created from the Resource sheets on pages 51–64. Give lots of praise for good attempts at spelling the words or parts of the words. Remind the child that each sentence should begin with a capital letter and end with a full stop. Once s/he has completed the two sentences you could ask her/him to colour the cars and to make up an extra sentence.

Name: **Date:**

Colour the bus red.

Colour the van blue.

Colour the lorry green.

Listen to your teacher. Write the sentences.

Notes for teachers

Encourage the child to spell words by segmenting them into their phonemes by dictating four sentences to her/him: *The bus is red. The van is blue. The lorry is green. The green lorry is next to the blue van.* The child is likely to need help with segmenting the words into their phonemes and you can provide further support helping her/him to copy the words from the instruction text or to look them up in the dictionary created from the Resource sheets on pages 51–64. Give lots of praise for good attempts at spelling the words or parts of the words. Remind the child that each sentence should begin with a capital letter and end with a full stop. Once s/he has completed the four sentences you could ask her/him to make up an extra sentence and to write it down.

Name: **Date:**

What is happening?

Notes for teachers

This sheet provides an excellent opportunity for creating a simple non-chronological text using interesting words and phrases. Read the question sentence with the child, pointing out that it starts with a capital letter and ends with a question mark. Discuss the picture, encouraging the child to describe the scene, what is happening and why it might be happening. Help her/him to compose some sentences then to write them on the writing lines. S/he could use the dictionary created from the Resource sheets on pages 51–64 to help with spelling.

Name: Date:

What is happening?

Notes for teachers

This sheet provides an excellent opportunity for creating a simple chronological text using interesting words and phrases. Read the question sentence with the child, pointing out that it starts with a capital letter and ends with a question mark. Discuss the picture, encouraging the child to describe the scene, what might have happened and what might happen next. Help her/him to compose some sentences then to write them on the writing lines. S/he could use the dictionary created from the Resource sheets on pages 51–64 to help with spelling.

Name: **Date:**

Look what happened a long time ago.

Now listen to your teacher. Write the sentences.

Notes for teachers

This sheet can be used as a follow up to Worksheet 18 and links with the Year 2 history topic, the Great Fire of London. Encourage the child to describe what s/he can see in the picture then read these sentences to her/him: *A long time ago there was a fire in London. It started in one street then lots of houses caught fire. The people had to get away. Some people got away in boats. We call the fire the great fire of London.*

Write out the words *London*, *started*, *caught*, *great* and *people* and show these words to the child. Now dictate the five sentences, helping the child to have a go at spelling most of the words by segmenting them into phonemes. Give lots of praise for success, even with just parts of words. For many children this is a very demanding activity and you may decide not to dictate all the sentences. Dictation is a very effective method for encouraging children to listen both to the phonemes within words and to the use of punctuation. The way in which we speak a sentence gives a clear indication of where a full stop should appear.

Name: Date:

Can you label this plant?

WORD BANK

pot

stem

leaf

roots

flower

Write two sentences about how a plant grows.

Notes for teachers

This worksheet provides practice in the vocabulary associated with the science topic, plants. Help the child to label the plant and the pot. Extend the activity by asking what a plant needs to help it grow. The child should be able to state that it needs water and light. Help the child to compose two sentences about how a plant grows e.g. The roots grow in the soil. The plant needs water to help it grow.

worksheet 21

Name: Date:

Can you label the picture?

WORD BANK

ground

trunk

roots

branch

leaf

Write three sentences about the tree.

Notes for teachers

This worksheet provides practice in the vocabulary associated with the science topic, plants. Help the child to label the tree and the ground. If possible, take the child to see a tree in the school grounds. Help the child to compose some sentences about a tree e.g. The tree is very tall. It has lots of green leaves. (Note that the word *leaves* is quite a complex plural. Discuss how the word *leaf* has been changed when we are talking about 'more than one' leaf.)

Name: Date:

Can you label the picture?

WORD BANK

- bulb
- wire
- battery
- bulb holder

Listen to your teacher. Write the sentences.

Notes for teachers

This worksheet provides practice in the vocabulary associated with the science topic, electricity. Help the child to label the items in the electrical circuit. If possible, show the child an electrical circuit like the one illustrated. Write down the words *light*, *lights* and *connected* for the child to see. Say each word slowly and carefully so that the child can hear the phonemes that make up the word. Dictate the following sentences for the child to write down: *The bulb is in a bulb holder. The bulb lights up when it is connected to the battery. There are two wires to connect the bulb to the battery.*

Name: Date:

Zipper eats healthy food.

He likes to eat apples, oranges, bananas and pineapples.

Colour the picture. Label the fruit.

Notes for teachers

This worksheet provides practice in the vocabulary associated with the science topic related to a healthy diet. Read the sentences to the child, using appropriate stresses and pauses to demonstrate the presence of the commas. Help the child to label the fruit. Encourage her/him to identify other healthy foods and to consider which foods are less healthy. As an introduction to Worksheet 24, discuss what the child likes to eat.

Name: **Date:**

worksheet 24

What do you like to eat?

Write about your favourite food.

Notes for teachers

Use this sheet after Worksheet 23. Help the child to write about their favourite food and drink. S/he may need to use commas if s/he has thought of a list of items. Although the word *favourite* is not included in the list of high frequency words identified for KS1, or in the medium frequency list for KS2, it is a very useful word for children to know and so is included in the dictionary created from the Resource sheets on pages 51–64.

Notes for teachers on Worksheets 25 to 33

The next seven worksheets feature a simple story concerning Zipper the alien. The activities will help the child to begin to create a piece of writing in a narrative form, possibly over several lessons.

Worksheets 25–29

The first four sheets each feature two pictures. (Note that one of the pictures forms the title page for the narrative story). Each sheet should be photocopied then cut in two so that the pictures can be introduced to the child one at a time and not necessarily in the correct order. In each case ask the child what the picture shows. This provides an excellent opportunity for practising speaking and listening skills. Praise the child for finding all the details in the picture.

Having discussed the pictures, photocopy and cut out the seven sentences on Worksheet 29. Read these with the child then help her/him to match the sentences to the pictures to make a story. This sequencing activity provides opportunities for lots of speaking and listening as well as considerable reading practice. You could discuss why Zipper went shopping on Saturday, why he packed his case and why he washed his spaceship.

The correct order of the sentences is as follows:

On Saturday Zipper goes shopping.
On Sunday Zipper packs his case.
On Monday Zipper washes his spaceship.
On Tuesday Zipper flies to the moon.
Zipper rests on Wednesday.
Zipper plays with his friends on Thursday.
On Friday Zipper flies back to earth.

Worksheets 30–31

Photocopy Worksheets 30 and 31 back to back on to a single sheet. This can then be folded to make a simple four-page book. Help the child to write sentences to go with the pictures on each page of their book. The child could simply copy the sentences provided or you could help her/him to compose her/his own sentences. If this is the case, encourage her/him to segment the words into their phonemes in order to spell them.

Worksheets 32–33

As a very useful extension activity, ask the child to create a four-page book about her/his own week using sheets 32 and 33. The child will need lots of help through speaking and listening. Discuss what s/he could be doing on each day of the week e.g. On Monday I do PE. On Tuesday I paint a picture. On Wednesday I use the computer.

Name: Date:

worksheet 25

worksheet 26

Name: **Date:**

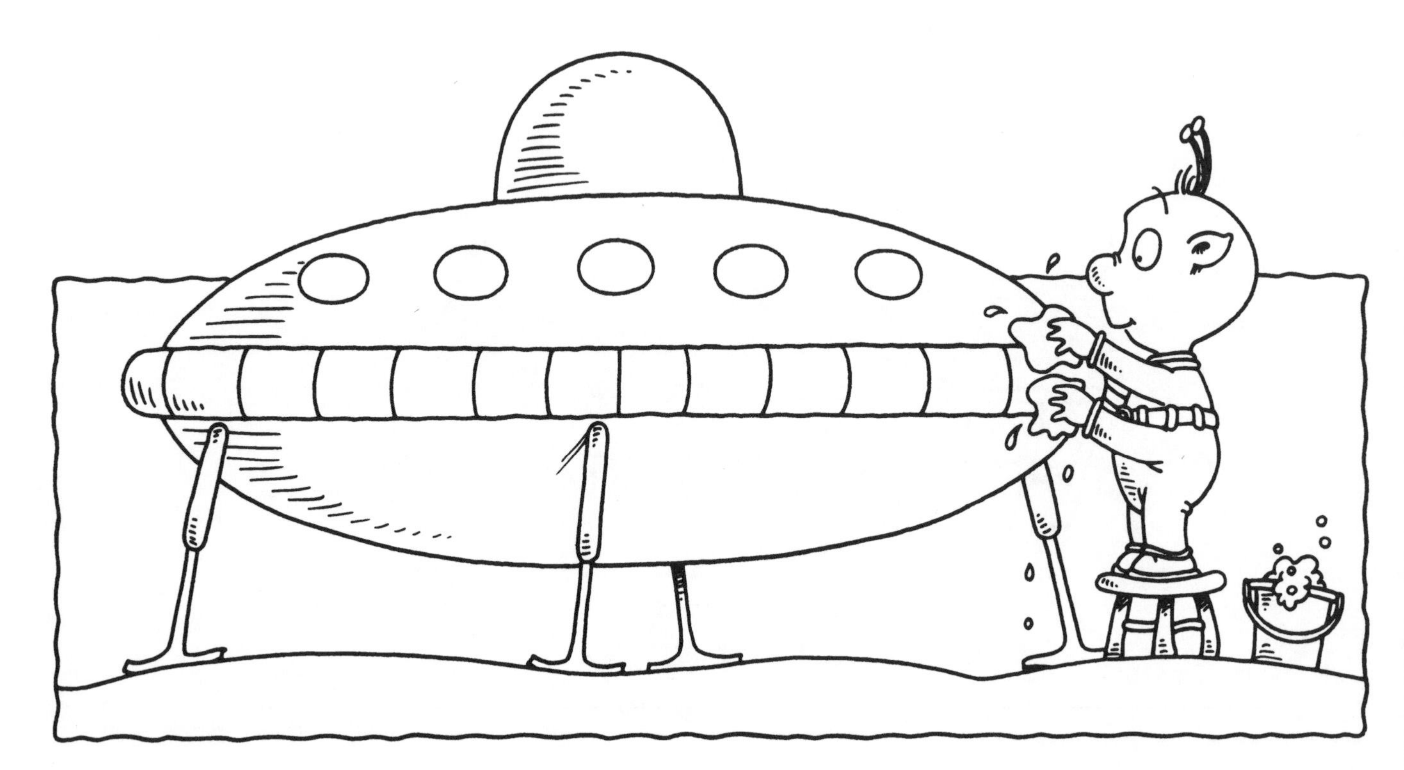

Name: **Date:**

worksheet 28

Name: Date:

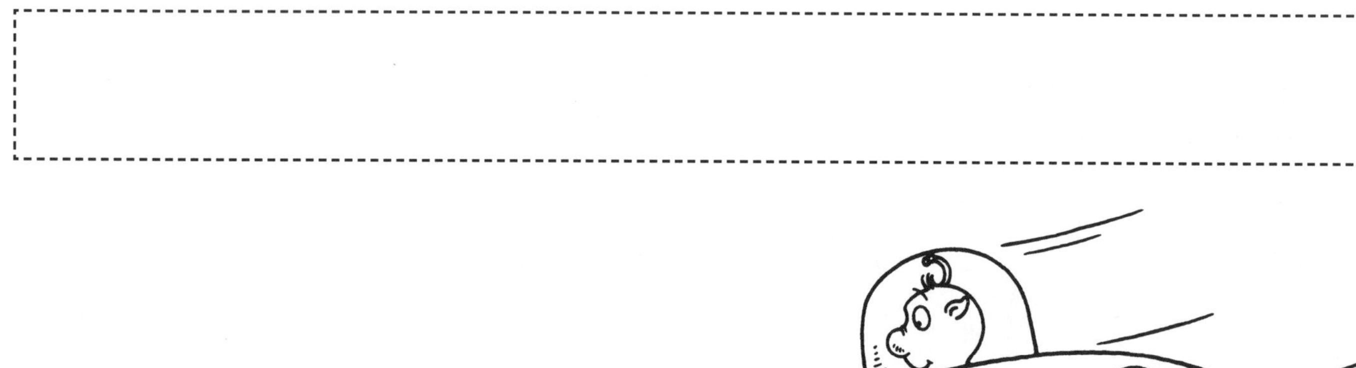

Name: Date:

On Saturday Zipper goes shopping.

On Sunday Zipper packs his case.

On Monday Zipper washes his spaceship.

On Tuesday Zipper flies to the moon.

Zipper rests on Wednesday.

Zipper plays with his friends on Thursday.

On Friday Zipper flies back to earth.

Worksheet 30
Zipper's week

31

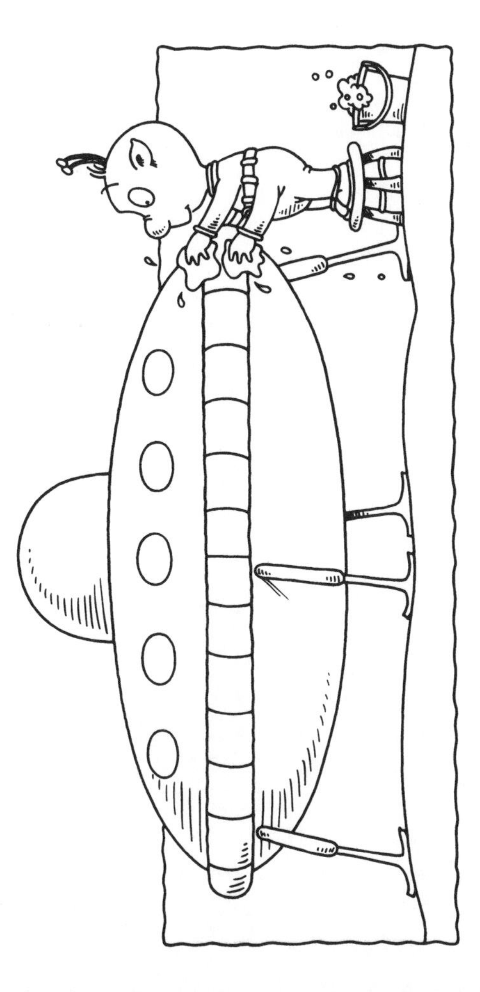

My week

by ____________________

On Saturday ____________________

____

On Thursday ____________________

____

On Friday ____________________

____

Worksheet 33

On Sunday ____________________

____

On Monday ____________________

____

On Tuesday ____________________

____

On Wednesday ____________________

____

Notes for teachers on Worksheets 34 to 40 and the Writing templates

The next seven worksheets feature the well-known fable of the hare and the tortoise by the Greek writer Aesop.

Worksheets 34–38

The first four sheets each feature two pictures. (Note that one of the pictures forms the title page for the narrative story). These sheets should be photocopied then cut in two so that the pictures can be introduced to the child one at a time and not necessarily in the correct order. In each case ask the child what the picture shows. This discussion provides an excellent opportunity for practising speaking and listening skills. Praise the child for finding all the details in the picture.

Having discussed the pictures, photocopy and cut out the seven pieces of text shown on Worksheet 38. Read these with the child, then help her/him to match them to the pictures to make a story. This sequencing activity provides opportunities for practising speaking and listening skills as well as considerable reading practice. You could discuss which animal would be expected to win the race, which one really won it and why. It would be helpful to explain to the children that this is a long race, like a marathon, rather than a race along a school running track.

The correct order of the pieces of writing is as follows:

The hare and the tortoise want a race.
The race starts and the hare starts running very fast.
The tortoise cannot run. He can walk slowly.
The hare is running very fast. He is hot and tired.
The hare is very tired. He goes to sleep.
The tortoise walks past the sleeping hare.
The tortoise wins the race.

Worksheets 39–40

Photocopy Worksheets 39 and 40 back to back on to a single sheet. This can then be folded to make a simple four-page book. Help the child to write sentences to go with the pictures on each page of their book. The child could simply copy the sentences that s/he has sequenced or you could help her/him to compose her/his own sentences. If this is the case, help her/him to segment the words into their phonemes to be able to spell them.

Writing templates

Writing template sheet 1 can be used for creating a four-page or eight-page book on any subject at any time. Simply photocopy this sheet on to both sides of a sheet of A4 paper then fold it to make a book, or use two sheets of A4 paper to make an eight-page book.

Writing template sheet 2 can be photocopied to make a one-page A4 story sheet to be used at any time that you would like the child to produce a narrative or non-narrative piece of writing. The child can draw a picture at the top of the sheet then use the writing lines to write her/his own story.

Name: Date:

worksheet 35

Name: **Date:**

Name: Date:

worksheet 36

worksheet 37

Name: **Date:**

Name: Date:

The hare and the tortoise want a race.

The race starts and the hare starts running very fast.

The tortoise cannot run. He can walk slowly.

The hare is running very fast. He is hot and tired.

The hare is very tired. He goes to sleep.

The tortoise walks past the sleeping hare.

The tortoise wins the race.

Worksheet 39

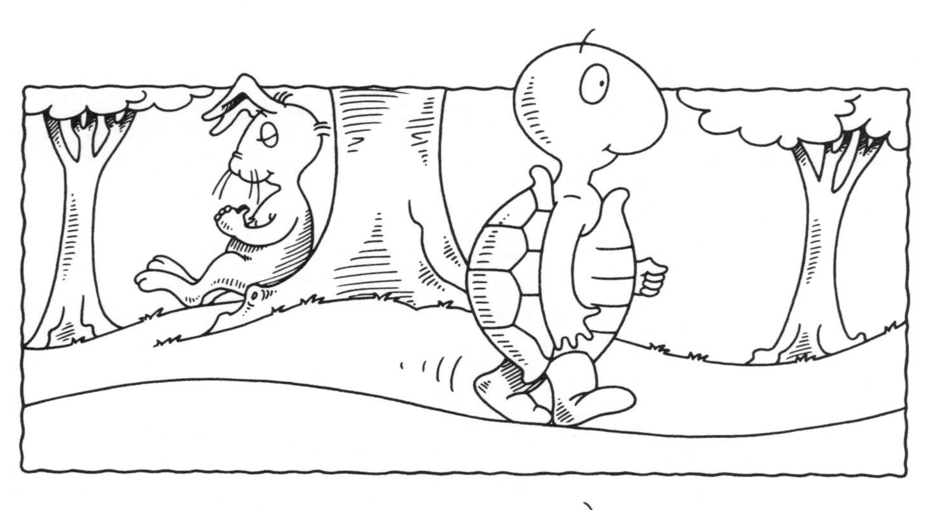

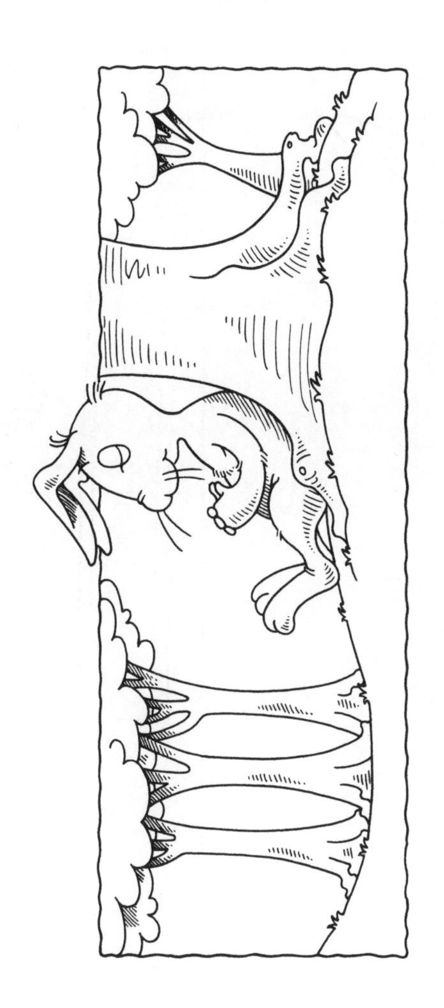

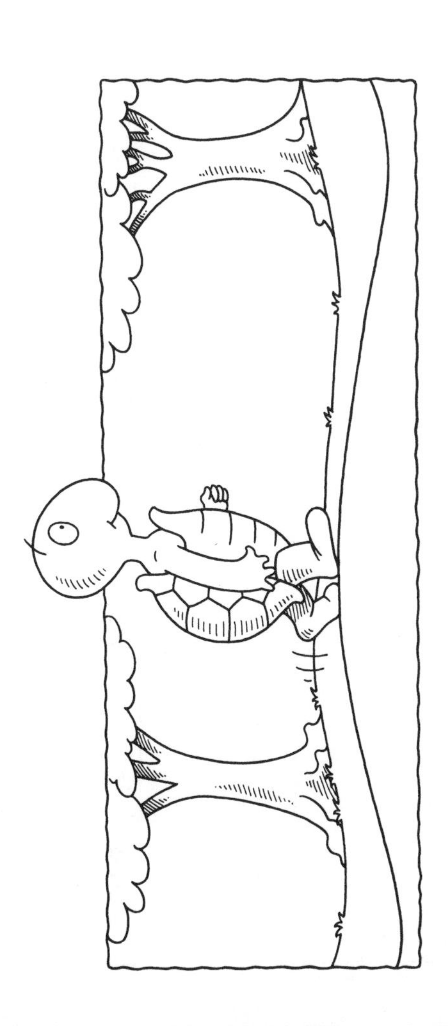

Writing template 1

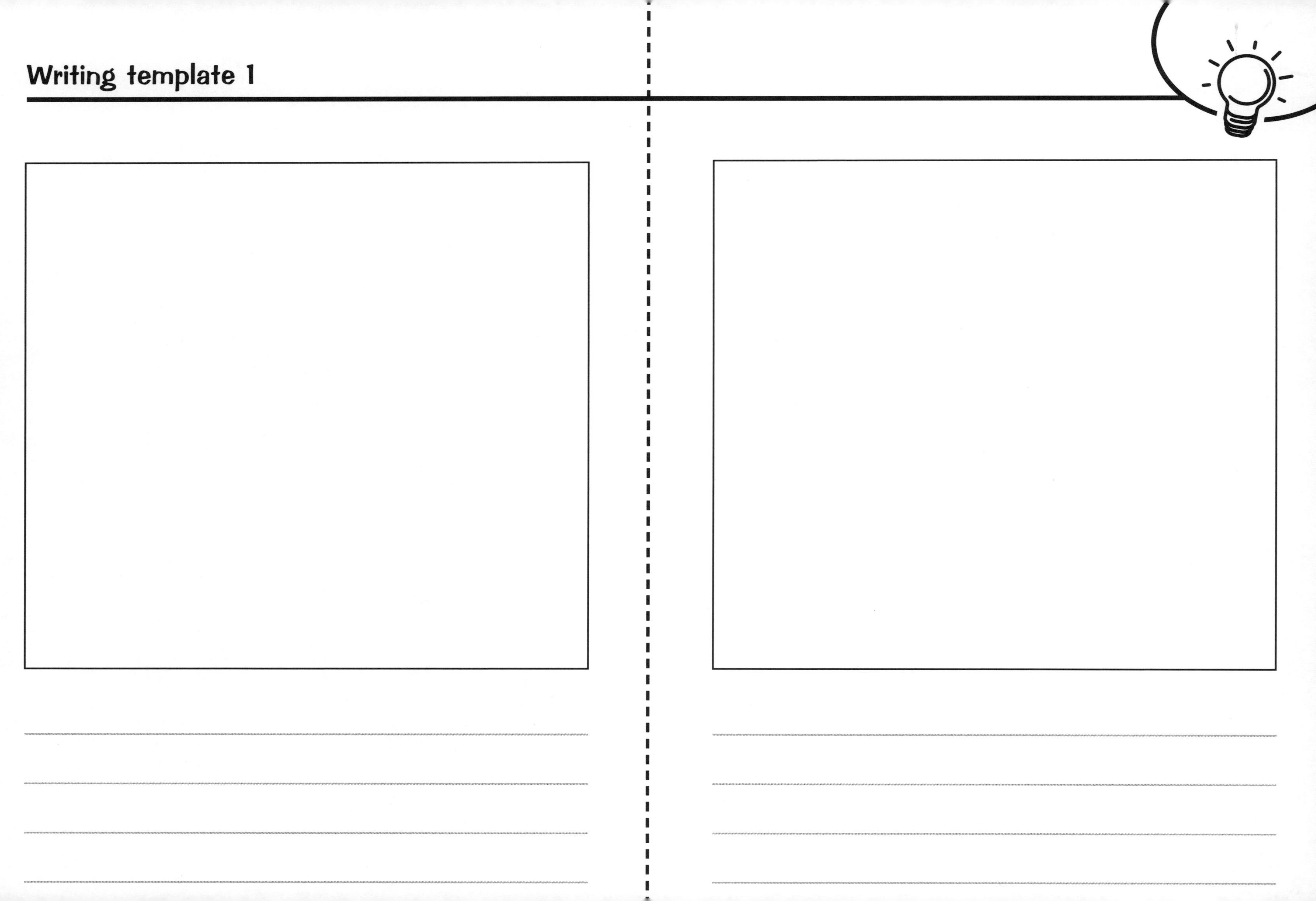

Writing template 2

Notes for teachers on the Dictionary resource sheets

The dictionary that can be created from the final fourteen pages of this book is a very valuable resource. It features all the high frequency words recommended for Reception, Year 1 and Year 2, together with many of the additional words used in this book. Photocopy the fourteen Dictionary resource sheets to create master copies then photocopy the master copies, back to back as follows:

Sheets 1/ 2 Sheets 3/4 Sheets 5/6 Sheets 7/8 Sheets 9/10 Sheets 11/12 Sheets 13/14

Each page of the dictionary has spaces for pupils to practise their own spellings. This is an excellent way of encouraging children to use their phonic knowledge to spell new words. When a child needs a word, help her/him to find the correct page of the dictionary, then ask her/him to attempt the word by segmenting it into its phonemes. Give the child lots of praise where s/he is successful even with part of a word, then write the word correctly on the line next to her/his attempt, stressing the phonemes and pointing out the graphemes that represent these.

Days	Months	Numbers
Monday	January	1 one
Tuesday	February	2 two
Wednesday	March	3 three
Thursday	April	4 four
Friday	May	5 five
Saturday	June	6 six
Sunday	July	7 seven
	August	8 eight
	September	9 nine
	October	10 ten
	November	11 eleven
	December	12 twelve
		13 thirteen
		14 fourteen
		15 fifteen
		16 sixteen
		17 seventeen
		18 eighteen
		19 nineteen
		20 twenty

Dictionary

Name ____________________

Dictionary resource sheet

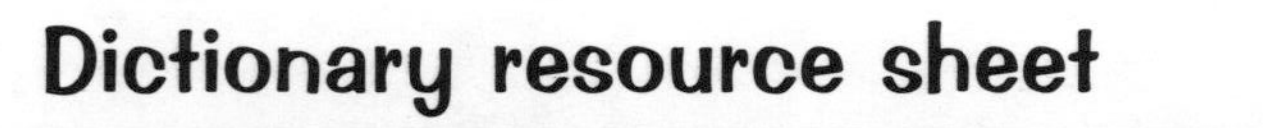

The alphabet

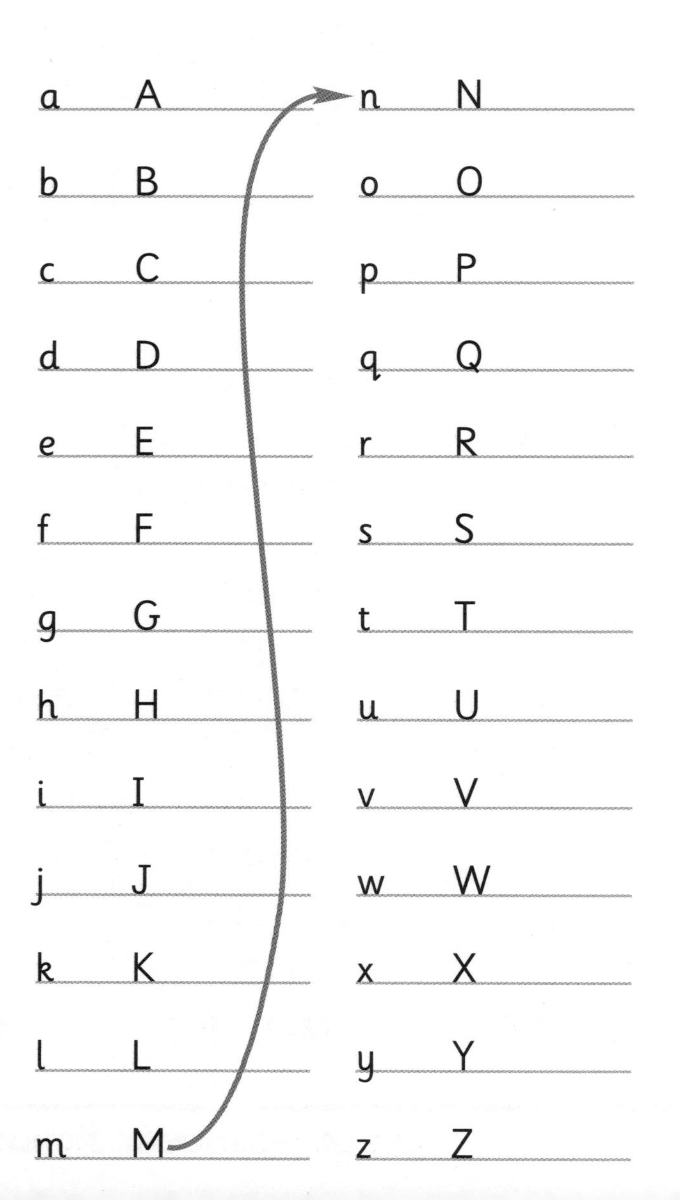

a	A	n	N
b	B	o	O
c	C	p	P
d	D	q	Q
e	E	r	R
f	F	s	S
g	G	t	T
h	H	u	U
i	I	v	V
j	J	w	W
k	K	x	X
l	L	y	Y
m	M	z	Z

Name ______________________

____

____

____

Address ______________________

____

____

____

____

____

____

Dictionary resource sheet

x X	y Y	z Z	a A		
	year	Zipper	a	as	
	yellow		about	at	
	yes		after	away	
	you		again		
	your		alien		
			all		
			am		
			an		
			and		
			another		
			apple		
			are		
			arm		

Dictionary resource sheet

b B

back	branch	
ball	brick	
banana	brother	
battery	brown	
be	bulb	
because	but	
bed	by	
been		
big		
black		
blue		
boat		
boy		

w W

want	will	
was	window	
water	wire	
way	with	
we	wood	
week	would	
went		
were		
what		
when		
where		
white		
who		

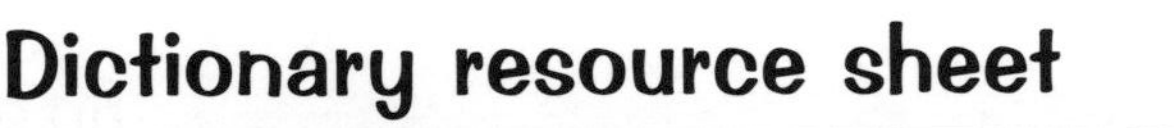

Dictionary resource sheet

v V

van

very

c C

call

called

came

can

can't

cat

come

comes

could

Dictionary resource sheet

d D

dad

day

did

dig

do

dog

don't

door

down

u U

up

us

Dictionary resource sheet

t T

take
than
that
the
their
them
then
there
these
they
this
three
tile
time
to
too
took
tree
trunk
two

e E

ear
eye

Dictionary resource sheet

f F

face

favourite

fire

first

flower

for

friendly

from

front

s S

said

saw

school

see

seen

she

should

sister

so

some

space

stem

Dictionary resource sheet

r R

ran

red

roof

roots

g G

get

girl

glass

go

going

good

got

green

ground

Dictionary resource sheet

h H

had

half

has

have

he

help

her

here

him

his

home

house

how

q Q

queen

quiet

Dictionary resource sheet

p P

people

pineapple

pink

play

pot

pull

purple

push

put

i I

I

if

in

is

it

Dictionary resource sheet

j J

jump

just

o O

of

off

old

on

once

one

or

orange

our

out

over

Dictionary resource sheet

n N

name

new

next

night

no

nose

not

now

k K

kind

king

Dictionary resource sheet

l L

ladder

last

laugh

leaf

leaves

leg

letterbox

like

little

live

lived

look

love

m M

made

make

man

many

may

me

more

mouth

much

mum

must

my